The Great Big
SEARCH
and FIND
Activity Book

Sandy Creek
NEW YORK

An imprint of Sterling Publishing Co., Inc.
1166 Avenue of the Americas
New York, NY 10036

ISBN 978-1-4351-6526-7

Manufactured in Guangdong, China
Lot #:
2 4 6 8 10 9 7 5 3 1
10/16

www.sterlingpublishing.com

Contents

Can you spot
these things?

apple core

sunblock

bowl of food

duck

Welcome to the World!

There's lots to see. Come and take a look!

North America

South America

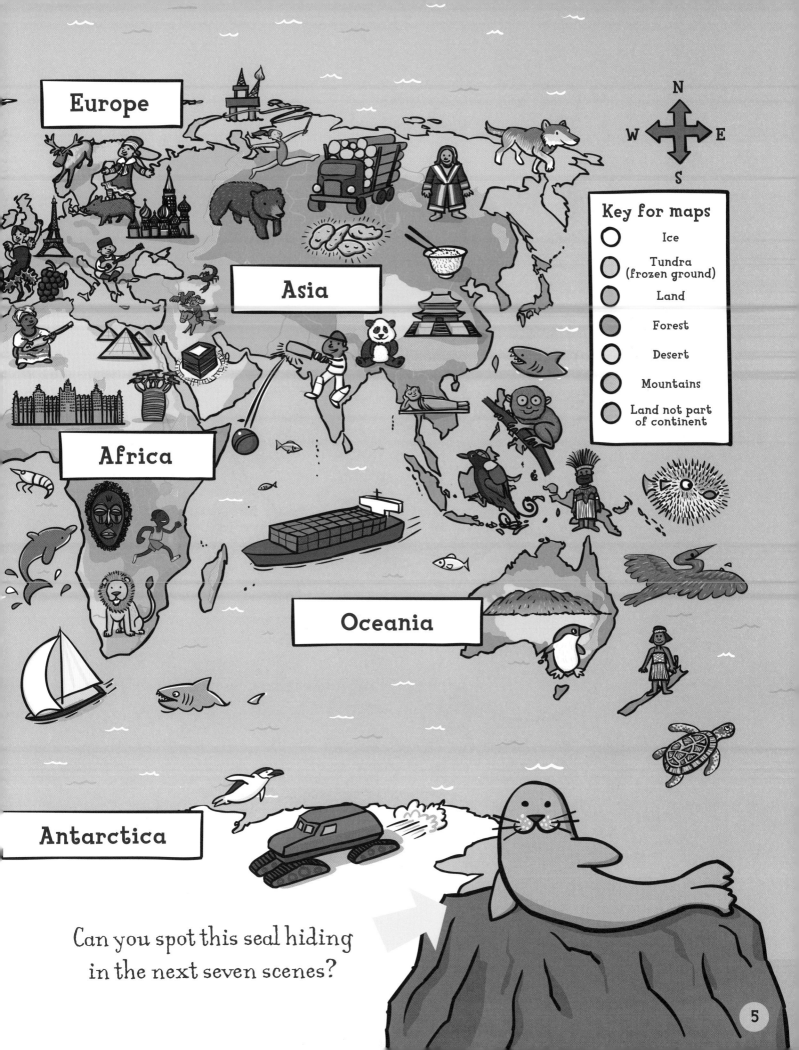

Europe

Asia

Africa

Oceania

Antarctica

Key for maps
- Ice
- Tundra (frozen ground)
- Land
- Forest
- Desert
- Mountains
- Land not part of continent

N
W E
S

Can you spot this seal hiding in the next seven scenes?

5

The Caribbean

Dominican Republic

Puerto Rico

Trinidad and Tobago

Cuba

Jamaica Haiti

Honduras

Nicaragua

Belize

Panama

Costa Rica

Guatemala

El Salvador

Mexico

PACIFIC OCEAN

There are ice fields in the far north and hot rainforests in the south.

North America is the only continent that has every type of climate.

Can you spot these things?

ox and cart

cactus

moose

piñata

Golden Gate Bridge

beaver

South America

Over a third of South America is covered by dripping green rainforest.

Venezuela

Guyana

Suriname

French Guiana

Colombia

Ecuador

Peru

Bolivia

Brazil

Europe

Europe has more than 50 countries. It includes the world's smallest country, Vatican City State, and half of the world's biggest country, Russia.

Iceland

United Kingdom

Ireland

NORTH ATLANTIC OCEAN

Netherlands

Belgium

Luxembourg

France

Switzerland

Portugal

Spain

Monaco

Andorra

Can you spot these things?

daffodil

lynx

waffle

race car

salamander

Africa

NORTH ATLANTIC OCEAN

Morocco

Western Sahara

Mauritania

Cape Verde

Senegal

The Gambia

Guinea-Bissau

Guinea

Sierra Leone

Liberia

Côte d'Ivoire

Ghana

Togo

Benin

Equatorial Guinea

Tunisia

Algeria

Libya

Mali

Niger

Chad

Burkina Faso

Nigeria

Cameroon

Central African Republic

Gabon

Congo

Angola

Namibia

Can you spot these things?

drum

elephant

penguin

gerbil

waterfall

SOUTH ATLANTIC OCEAN

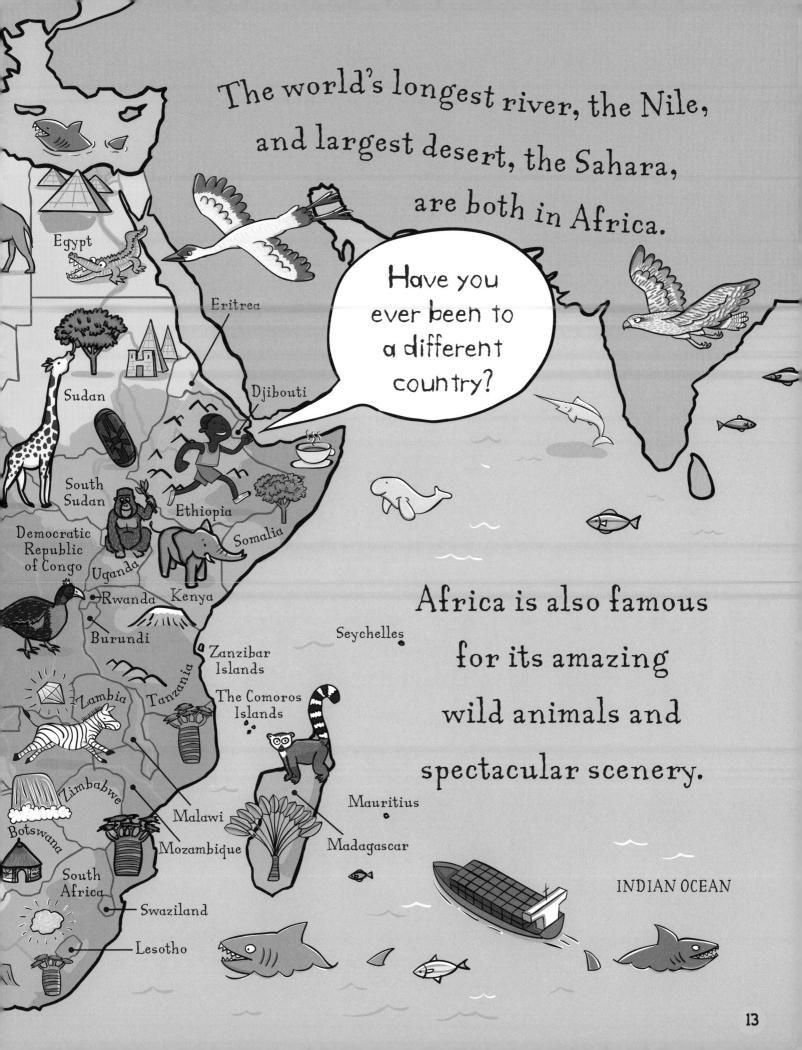

The world's longest river, the Nile, and largest desert, the Sahara, are both in Africa.

Have you ever been to a different country?

Africa is also famous for its amazing wild animals and spectacular scenery.

Egypt

Eritrea

Djibouti

Sudan

South Sudan

Ethiopia

Somalia

Democratic Republic of Congo

Uganda

Rwanda

Kenya

Burundi

Seychelles

Zanzibar Islands

Tanzania

The Comoros Islands

Zambia

Zimbabwe

Malawi

Mauritius

Botswana

Mozambique

Madagascar

South Africa

Swaziland

Lesotho

INDIAN OCEAN

Asia

Can you spot these things?

Marco Polo sheep

tarsier

orangutan

coffee

camel

scorpion

Georgia

Azerbaijan

Kazakhstan

Turkey

Armenia

Uzbekistan

Kyrgyzstan

Lebanon

Israel

Syria

Turkmenistan

Tajikistan

Jordan

Iraq

Iran

Afghanistan

Kuwait

United Arab Emirates

Nepal

Bahrain

Qatar

Pakistan

Saudi Arabia

India

Yemen

Oman

Maldives

Sri Lanka

Oceania

Papua New Guinea

INDIAN OCEAN

GREAT BARRIER REEF

Australia

Many of Australia's animals don't live wild on any other continent.

Tasmania

Can you spot these things?

kiwi fruit   didgeridoo   headdress   sheep   platypus

16

Nauru

Kiribati

Solomon Islands

Tuvalu

PACIFIC OCEAN

Tokelau

Wallis and Futuna

Samoa

Vanuatu

French Polynesia

Fiji

New
Caledonia

Niue

Tonga

Cook Islands

Oceania is made up of more
than 10,000 islands.

New Zealanders
love rugby. What's
your favorite
sport?

New Zealand

The Great Barrier Reef
is the only living thing
you can see from space!

Antarctica

Halley research station (UK)

Amundsen-Scott research station (USA)

SOUTH POLE

SOUTH PACIFIC OCEAN

SOUTHERN OCEAN

Antarctica is a frozen land mostly covered by ice. Near the center is the South Pole.

Which Brazilian dancer is different?

Find 10 differences between these two globes...

We're on the Move

There's lots to see.
Come and take a look!

Trailer park

Bus

Bicycle lane

Subway

There are lots of ways to get around.
What is your favorite way to travel?

Airport

Harbor

Ferry

Spaghetti junction

Trains

This little mouse is hiding. Can you find it in the next six scenes?

Can you spot these things?

driver   motorcycle   clock   rowboat   lifeboat

Can you spot these things?

blue flag   orange chairs   anchor   life ring   green car

The world's largest ferries can carry 230 cars and 1,200 passengers!

Have you ever been on a ferry?

How many yellow vehicles can you see?

Can you spot these things?

sign · traffic cone · helicopter · police car · apple

In some big cities, lots of roads cross over each other—they are called spaghetti junctions. In Shanghai, China, six roads cross over each other in this way.

HAULAGE

POLICE

REMOVALS

6 ASL

A travel trailer is a small
home on wheels that can
be towed behind a car.
A camper van can be driven.

The world's smallest travel trailer is only
slightly larger than a single bed!

Can you spot these things?

bench   balloon   stroller   newspaper   guitar

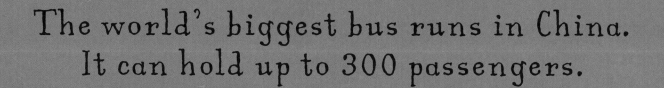

The world's biggest bus runs in China.
It can hold up to 300 passengers.

The world's busiest airport is in Atlanta, Georgia. More than 101 million people pass through it each year.

Did you know that the tips of a plane's wings bend upward when the plane takes off?

Which container ship is different?

Find 10 differences between these two traffic scenes...

Watch Out! There are Dinosaurs About

Supersaurus

Triceratops

Stegosaurus

Have fun coloring in Dinosaur Island.
Use lots of colors!

Pterosaurs

Plant Eaters

Velociraptor

Eggs

Plesiosaurs

Can you spot this baby Tyrannosaurus rex (say Tie-ran-uh-sore-us rex) in the next six scenes?

Supersaurus
(say *Super-sore-us*)
was one of the
biggest dinosaurs.

The giant *Supersaurus* was as long as
10 elephants standing in a line!

What is the Supersaurus eating?

Can you spot these things?

waterfall   pink rock   log   dragonfly   yellow flower

Can you spot these things?

red lizard   palm tree   cactus   feather   bones

The name *Velociraptor* (say *Vell-oss-ee-rap-tor*) means "speedy robber." This little dinosaur could run very fast.

All baby dinosaurs—even the really big ones—started life by hatching out of eggs.

Make your own baby dinosaur!

Carefully decorate half of an empty, clean eggshell with felt-tip pens. Make a dinosaur head and neck out of modeling clay. Mark the eyes and mouth with a pencil. Place the dinosaur inside the shell so that its face is peeping out.

Can you find my twin? He looks just like me!

Can you find and color these things?

dinosaur triplets

spotted egg

frilled dinosaur

spiky tail

baby dinosaur

Have fun coloring in all these dinosaur eggs. Use lots of colors!

Although some dinosaurs ate meat, most were plant eaters.

Can you spot these things?

red fish   fern   pine cone   pink flower   snake

Stegosaurus (say *Steg-uh-sore-us*) had huge, bony plates along its back and spikes on its tail that were as long as swords!

How many spikes do I have at the end of my tail?

Have fun coloring in all these stomping dinosaurs!

Can you find and color these things?

lizard

tree stump

fish

butterfly

eggshell

People who hunt for fossils are called paleontologists (say *pal-ee-ont-ol-o-jists*).

Can you spot these things?

hammer

tape measure

brush

drink bottle

camera

Which *Velociraptor* is different?

Did You Know?

Of course, Dinosaur Island isn't a real place. Lots of these dinosaurs lived millions of years apart and so they would never have met.

Some of the dinosaurs' closest relatives are still around today. You might see one if you look out of your window. They're birds!

No one is certain what colors dinosaurs were, but we know that some had feathers and most of them had scaly skin.

One of the biggest dinosaurs that we know about is the gigantic *Argentinosaurus* (say *Ar-gen-teen-oh-sore-us*). Maybe someone will discover an even bigger one soon!

Anyone can look for dinosaur fossils. One of the first fossil hunters was a little girl named Mary Anning, who lived in England about 200 years ago.

Creatures of the Ocean

Find out who lives in our watery world.

Whale sharks

Sea horses

Coral reef

Octopuses

Have fun coloring in all the strange creatures of the ocean. Use lots of colors!

Beach

Arctic waters

Dolphins

Strange ocean creatures

Can you find this baby shark hiding in the next six ocean scenes?

Deep sea

Can you find and color these things?

sea horse   fish   diver   turtle   seal

Whale sharks are the world's biggest fish. They are huge, but harmless to humans.

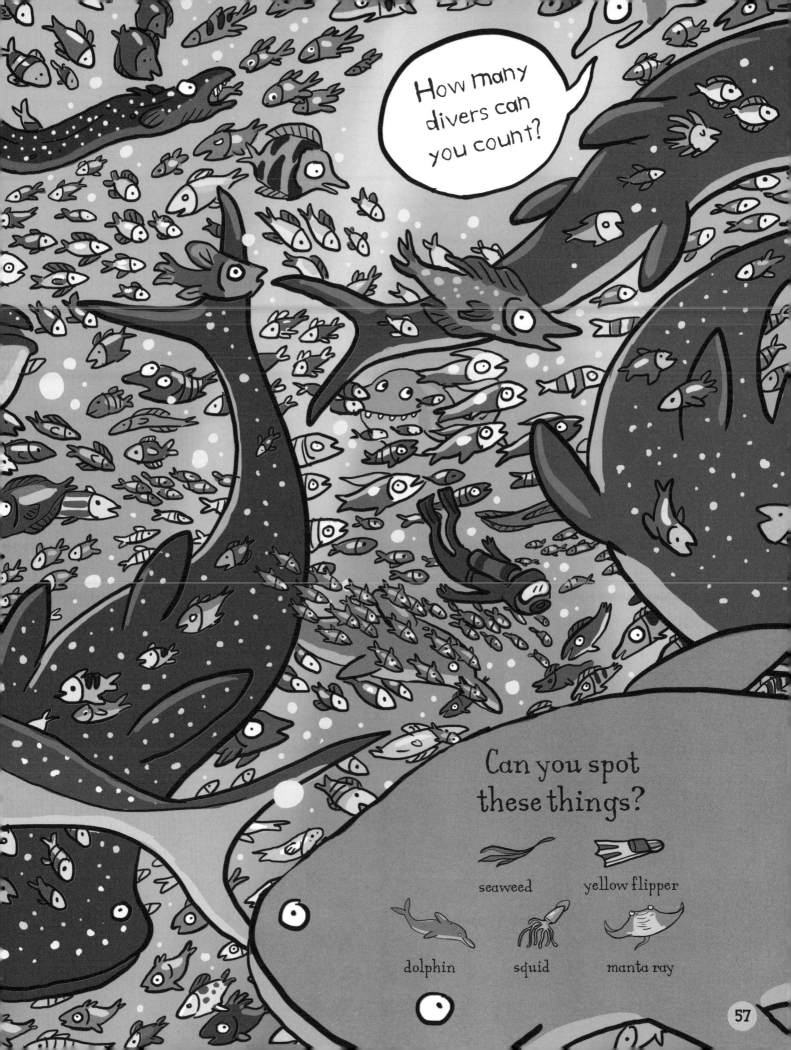

Can you find and color these things?

starfish   clam   anchor

sea cucumber   eel

Sea horses are little fish with tiny fins that swim upright very slowly through the water.

Some of the most beautiful fish in the world live on the Great Barrier Reef near Australia.

In winter polar bears live on the ice that covers the ocean around the North Pole.

Can you find and color these things?

 sailboat

whale

reindeer

sleeping musk ox

walrus

Turtles live in the ocean but lay their eggs on the beach. When the baby turtles hatch, they have to crawl to the sea!

Can you spot these things?

sign

eggs

pelican

pink shell

blue crab

Some ocean creatures look very strange indeed!

Can you spot these things?

blobfish   puffer fish   yeti crab   monkfish   parrot fish

Which sea horse is different?

Find 10 differences between these two underwater scenes...

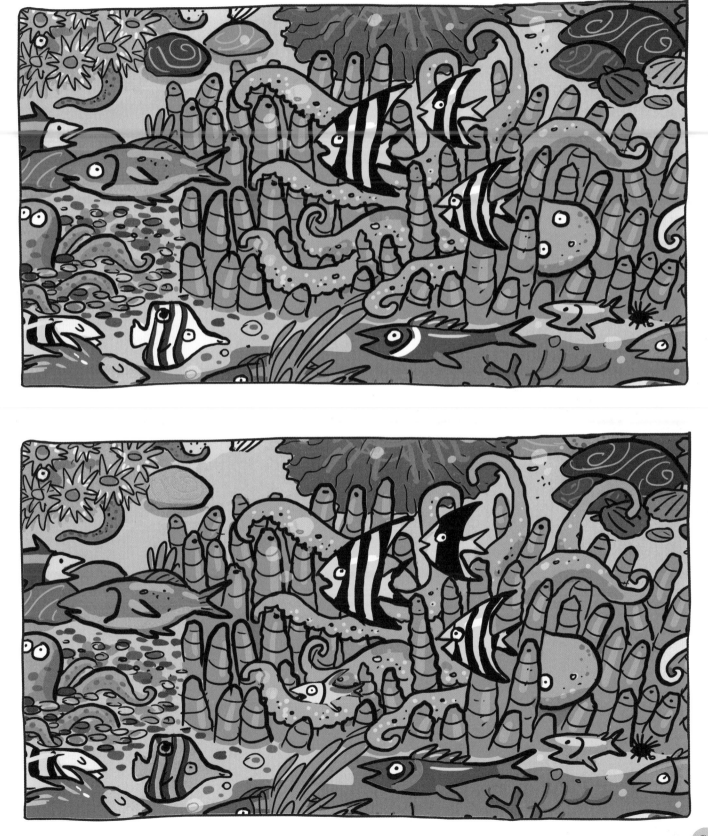

Crocodiles often sleep with their mouths open. Sometimes little birds fly in and pick meat off their teeth!

Can you find and color these things?

ladybug   dolphin   bird   crocodile nest   frog

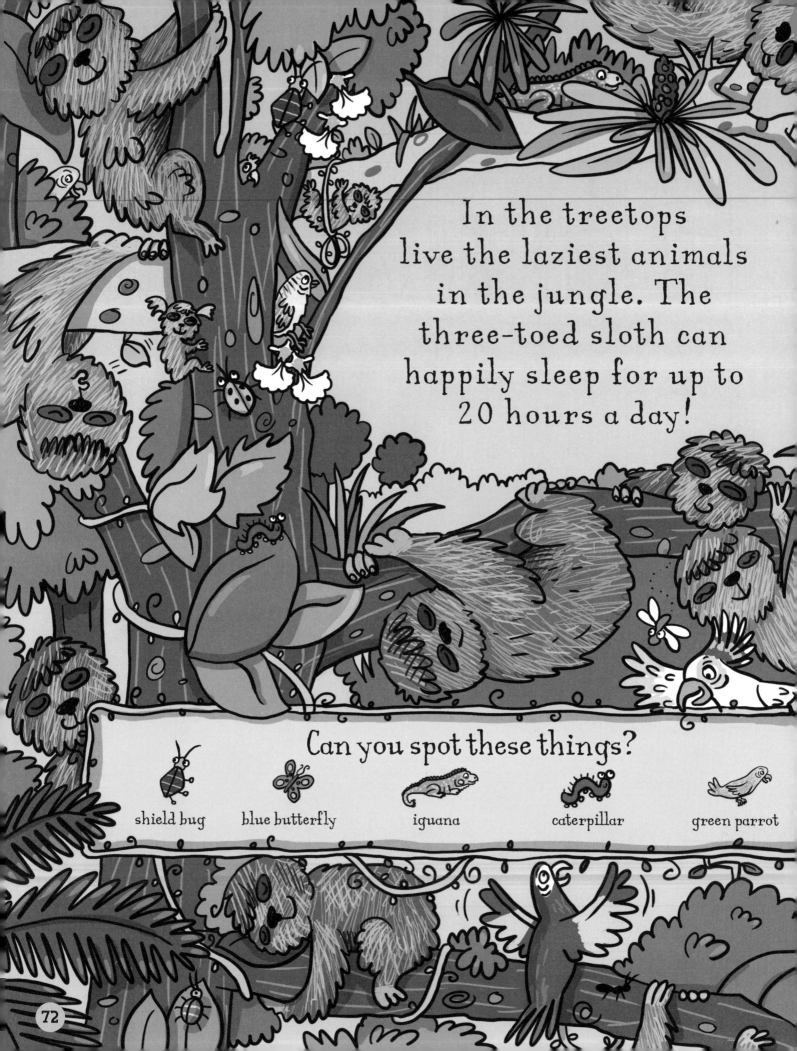

In the treetops live the laziest animals in the jungle. The three-toed sloth can happily sleep for up to 20 hours a day!

Can you spot these things?

shield bug   blue butterfly   iguana   caterpillar   green parrot

Poison dart frogs are beautiful but very dangerous!

Some poison dart frogs have enough poison to kill 10 people!

Can you find three pairs of matching frogs?

Can you spot these things?

scissors caterpillar cocoa pod red spider beetle

In the rainy jungle, orangutans hold
leaves over their nests to keep them dry!

Have fun coloring in this stormy jungle scene. Use lots of colors!

Can you see two baby orangutans?

Can you find and color these things?

sun bear   camera   binoculars   tiger cub   map

Tapirs have hooves and long noses.
The babies have spots and stripes.

Can you spot these things? log yellow flowers vine white bird red butterfly

78

Spots and stripes can help animals to blend in with their surroundings and keep them safe.

Can you spot the baby tapir?

At night some creatures sleep, while others come out to hunt for food.

Which crocodile is different?

Find 10 differences between these two jungle scenes...

Down on the Farm
There's lots to see. Come and take a look!

Farmhouse

Vegetable patch

Pigsty

Chickens

Have fun coloring in this busy farm scene. Use lots of colors!

Farm vehicles

Sheep

Wheat

Cows

Stables

Can you find this little lamb hiding in the next five farm scenes?

Can you spot these things?

donkey   underpants   mole   spoon   bell

Can you find and color these things?

cat   flower   frog   kettle   shoe

Cock-a-doodle-doo!

There are lots of different farm animals on this farm.

Bread, pasta, and cereals are often made from wheat.

How many mice are hiding in the field?

Can you spot these things?

worm   bee   spider   beetle   daisy

Can you spot these things?

watch   scales   tire   comb   sock

A sheep's fleecy coat can be used to make wool.

Can you find and color these things?

umbrella   book   trampoline   dragonfly   towel

Color in all the piglets!

Pigs roll in mud to help them cool down!

Which pig is different?

Find 10 differences between these two vegetable patches...

Mall

Airport

Rush hour

Park

Train station

Fire station

Can you spot this puppy hiding in the next six busy city scenes?

More people live in Tokyo, Japan, than in any other city in the world.

Fire engines have sirens and flashing lights so people know to move out of their way.

105

Can you spot these things?

striped kite

teddy bear

basket

lily pad

bin

ice cream

TICKETS

The world's biggest mall is in Dubai, UAE. It has 1,200 shops!

More to Color

Finish drawing the pictures
using the grid to help you.
Then color them in!

Did you find me?

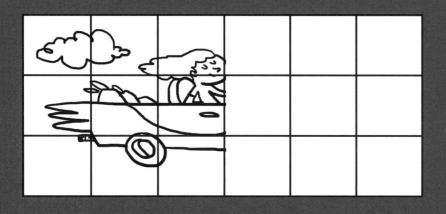

Find 10 differences between these two houses...

Marvel at the Museum

There's lots to see. Come and take a look!

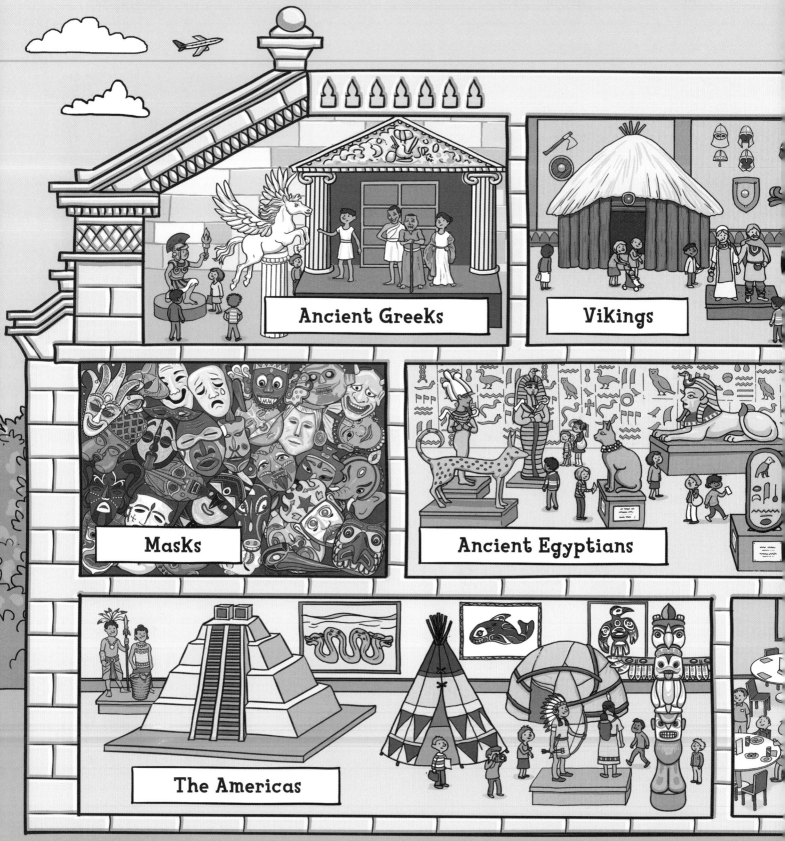

Ancient Greeks

Vikings

Masks

Ancient Egyptians

The Americas

Can you spot these things?

mask · warrior · shield · visitor · sphinx head

Buried treasure

Ancient Romans

Dinosaurs

Gift shop and café

Can you spot this mummy hiding in the next five museum scenes?

Dinosaur fossils are displayed in museums.
This dinosaur was as long as three buses!

Can you spot these things?

canopic jar · owl · shopping bag · necklace · bird

Look for Egypt on a map!

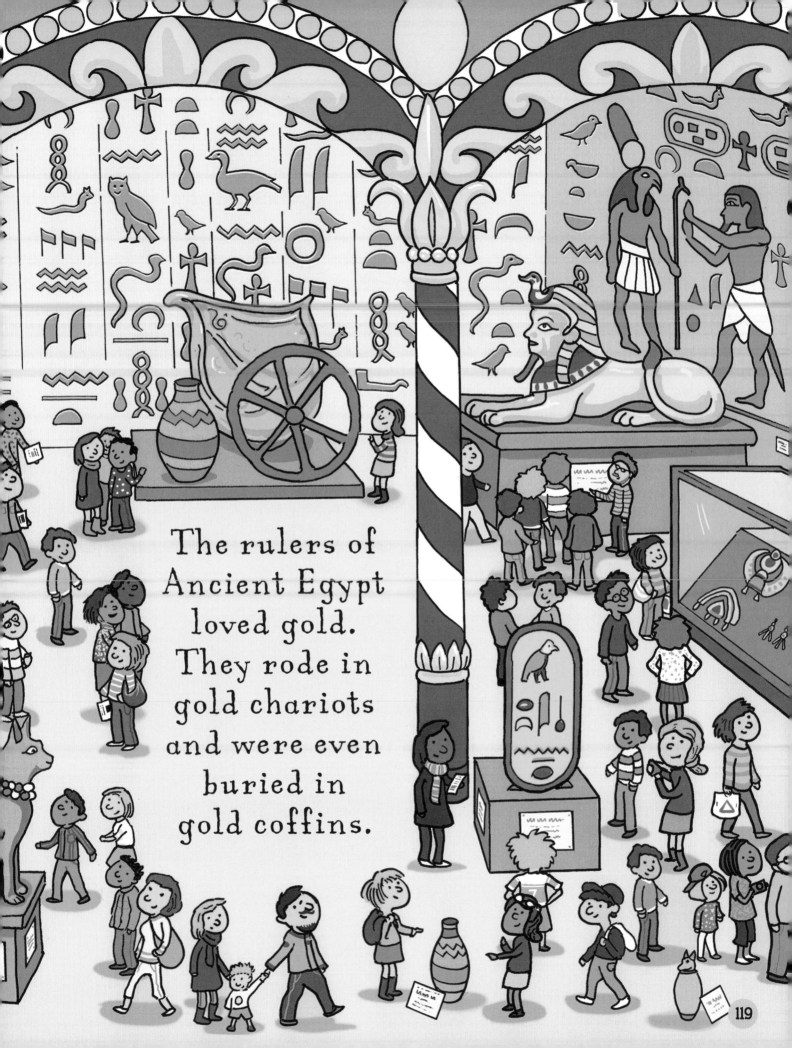

The rulers of Ancient Egypt loved gold. They rode in gold chariots and were even buried in gold coffins.

The Ancient Greeks thought that art, writing, and drama were very important.

One Ancient Greek story is about a winged horse named Pegasus.

The Ancient Romans loved entertainment. They held parties and feasts at home and went out to see chariot races and gladiator fights.

The Vikings lived more than 1,000 years ago. They traveled to different countries all over Europe in boats called longships.

Which totem pole is different?

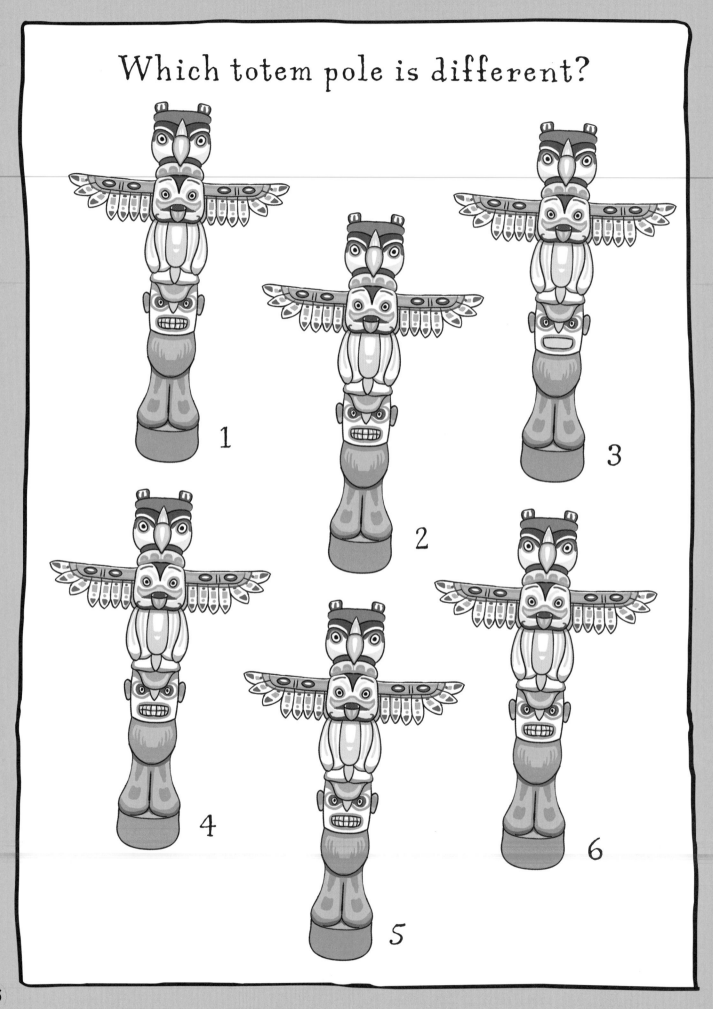

Did You Know?

The word dinosaur comes from the Greek language and means "terrible lizard."

Ancient Romans loved eating exotic things such as swans, crows, horses, peacocks, and dormice.

The ancient people of Mexico believed in worshiping the Sun to give it enough strength to rise each day.

Some of the first people to wear jewelry were men. They wore chains and bracelets to show how rich they were and to bring them luck in battle.

The Ancient Egyptians invented lots of things we use today, such as paper, pens, locks, keys, and even toothpaste!

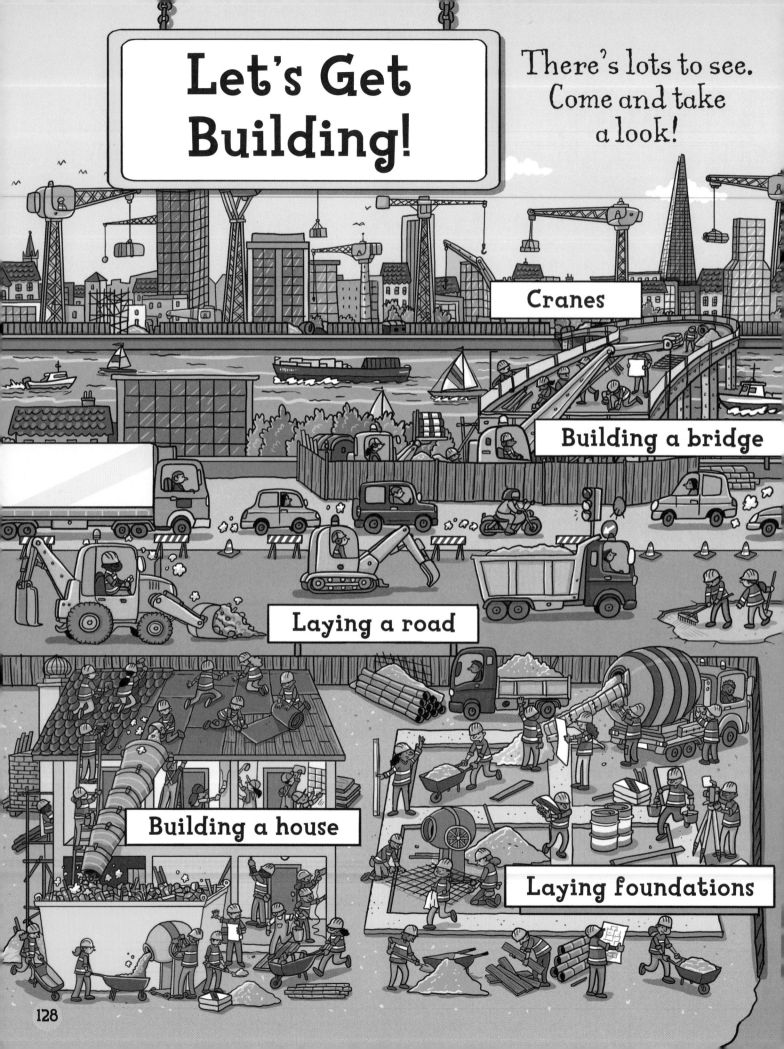

Let's Get Building!

There's lots to see. Come and take a look!

Cranes

Building a bridge

Laying a road

Building a house

Laying foundations

128

Can you spot these things?

roofer   oil drums   builder   builder with wheelbarrow   green jug

Demolition site

Diggers

Theme park

Playground

Can you spot this bird hiding in the next six scenes?

129

Houses are built on foundations that are dug into the ground. Foundations stop houses from sinking or falling over.

A building site can be dangerous, so builders wear hard hats to keep them safe.

Can you spot these things?

chair

level

hook

wire cutters

flask

Can you spot these things?

shower head screwdriver pink helmet cement trowel hammer

Can you spot these things?

rake

spare tire

traffic lights

red flag

pneumatic drill

The longest over-water bridge is in China. It took 10,000 workers over four years to build it.

Who has dropped a sandwich over the side of the bridge?

Can you spot these things?

blue power drill   kayak   plans   buoy   airplane

Old buildings can be knocked down by wrecking balls or blown up with explosives.

There are many different types of digger. One type is called a backhoe loader. It has a bucket and arm at the back and a shovel, or loader, at the front.

Diggers can be very noisy, so drivers wear earmuffs to protect their ears.

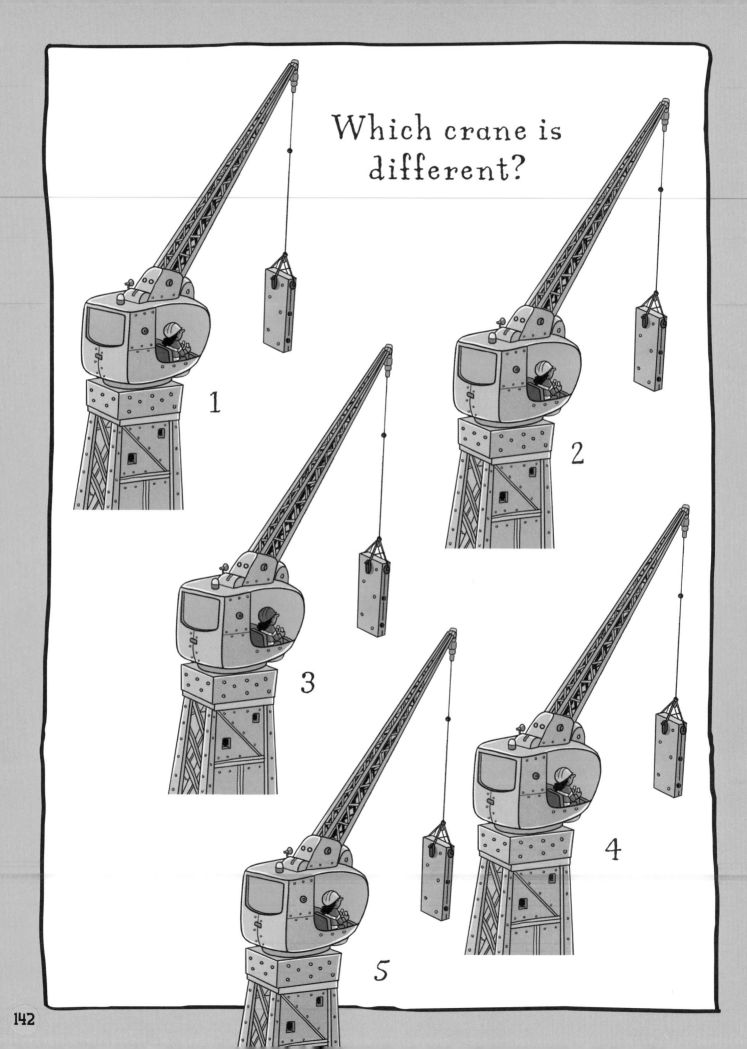

Which crane is different?

Did You Know?

The Chrysler Building, a 77-story skyscraper in New York City, was built very quickly. Four stories were completed every week.

It takes just 15 seconds for a 30-story building to be demolished using explosives.

The Shard in London, UK, is more than 984 feet tall and has 95 stories. The average elevator speed is 20 feet per second so you can get to the top in less than a minute!

The Ancient Greeks invented cranes more than 2,000 years ago to help them build stone temples.

Who's at the Zoo?

Butterfly house

Penguins

Elephants

Gorillas

Bugs and reptiles

Aquarium

Have fun coloring in the zoo. Use lots of colors!

African plain

Big cats

Birds

Can you spot this zebra hiding among the animals in the next five zoo scenes?

Can you find and color these things?

beetle   fish   ice cream   frog   ostrich

Penguins sometimes slide on their tummies! This is called tobogganing.

Lions are the only big cats that live in groups.

Have fun coloring in the birds!

Young flamingoes have gray feathers.
Color some of them gray!

Can you find and color these things?

boat   worm   necklace   dragonfly   mirror

Gorillas sleep in
nests high up
in the trees.

More to Spot

Go back and find these scenes on the zoo pages!

Did you find me?

Find 10 differences between these two elephant scenes...

A Garden to Explore

Have fun coloring in all the
different parts of the garden.
Use lots of colors!

Can you spot this snail hiding in the next six scenes?

Bees

Ants

Lawn

Birds

Ants are small but strong. They work together to find food and build nests.

Where do you think the ants' nest is?

Can you spot these things?

earwig   daisy   centipede   trowel   seeds

Can you spot
these things?

wood louse

candle

grasshopper

crown

toy car

163

Can you find and color these things?

 carrots   squash small fork big tomato   watering can

Have fun coloring in all the vegetables in this garden. Use lots of colors!

Caterpillars must eat as much as they can before they turn into butterflies.

How many holes has the caterpillar made in this lettuce leaf?

Can you spot these things?

spider's web   pinecone   toadstool   green apple   red flower

Squirrels build their homes in trees using twigs and moss. A squirrel's nest is called a drey.

How many squirrels can you count?

Bees do a special dance to tell one another where the best flowers are.

169

At night the yard is still full of life. You can often see foxes playing on the grass!

Have fun coloring this nighttime yard. Add a yellow glow to the lights!

Which picture is different?

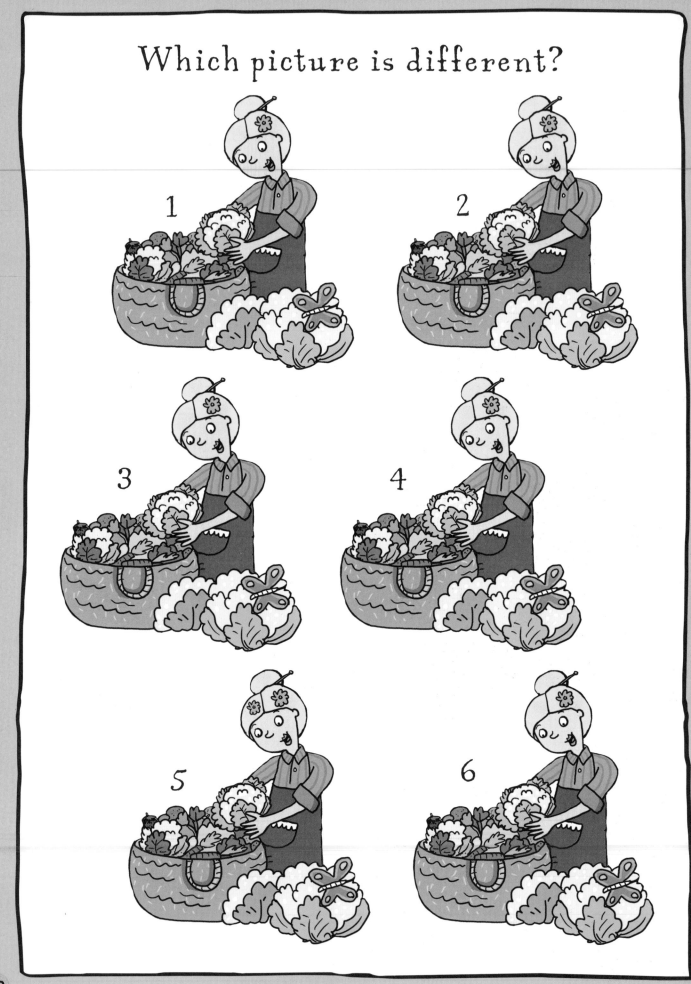

Find 10 differences between these two garden scenes...

3, 2, 1, Blast Off to Space!

Have fun coloring in all
the weird and wonderful things
in space. Use lots of colors!

Earth

Mars

Our Solar System

Planet Zorgoop!

Can you find and color these things?

house   two-headed alien   rocket   umbrella   three-eyed alien

Can you spot this robot hiding in the next six space scenes?

175

The first person to go to space was Yuri Gagarin from Russia.

Because there is no gravity in space, everything floats!

Can you spot these things?

donut apple toothbrush sock glasses

Make your own robot!

Using an empty toilet tube, small boxes, and aluminum foil, make your own robot. Use tape to join all the parts together, and then cover them in foil. You could use stickers to add buttons, controls, and a face.

Our Solar System includes the Sun and eight planets that orbit around it.

Scientists think that astronauts will be able to land on Mars by 2040.

Can you spot these things?

dustpan

soccer ball

cupcake

ladder

flag

Can you find and color these things?

three-eyed alien

green alien

UFO

lamp

traffic lights

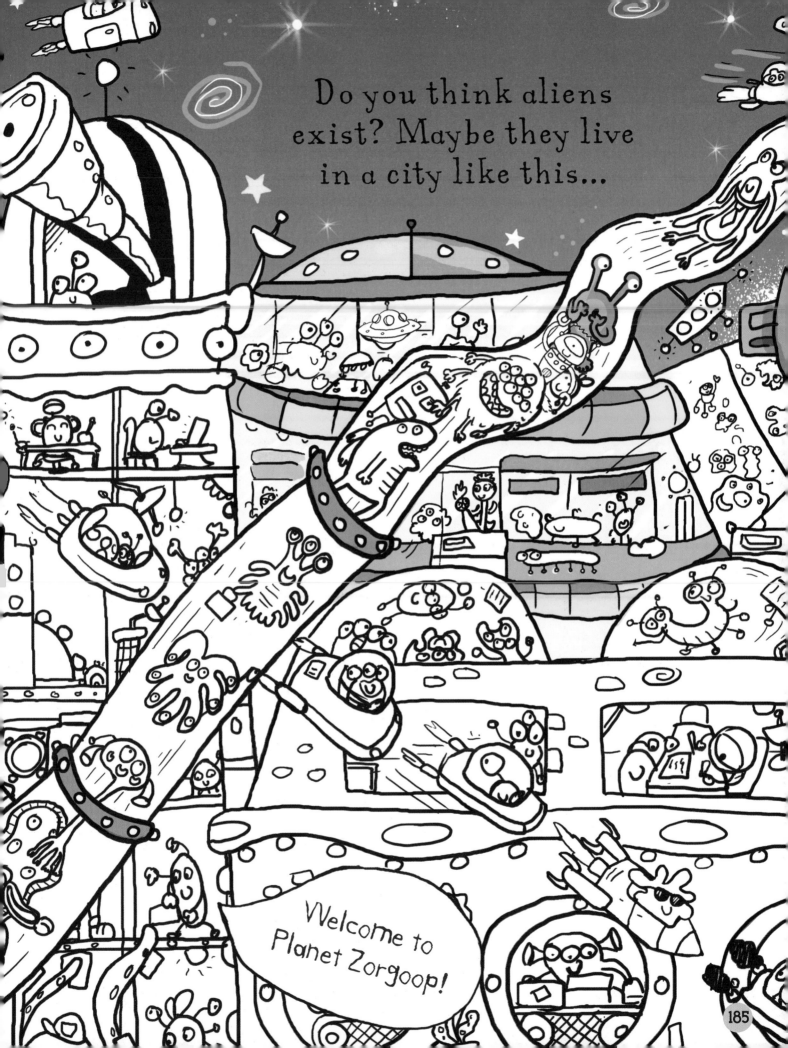

Which alien is different?

Find 10 differences between these two alien scenes...

Answers

Welcome to the World!
6-7 There are four bears.

14-15
Spot the
twin

18-19 There are four boats.

20

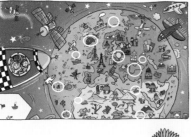

21 Two is the odd one out.

We're On the Move
24-25 There are seven yellow vehicles.

28-29 There are five dogs.

30 There are seven windows on the train.

36 Six is the
odd one out.

37

Watch Out! There are Dinosaurs About
41 *Supersaurus* is eating leaves.

42-43 There are four purple dinosaurs.

44-45
Spot the
twin

48 The dinosaur has four spikes
on its tail.

52 Five is the
odd one out.

Creatures of the Ocean
56-57 There are four divers.

62-63 There are 18 bears.

64-65

68 Five is the odd one out.

69

Step into the Jungle
72-73
Which
sloth is
not
asleep?

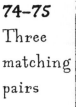

74-75 Three matching pairs

76-77 Spot two babies

78-79

80-81 There are eight bats.

82 Five is the odd one out.

83

Down on the Farm

88-89 There are seven ducklings.

90-91 There are four mice.

96 Four is the odd one out.

97

Get Busy in the City

100-101 Spot the bus stop

102-103 Ten firefighters are wearing helmets.

104-105 There are four airplanes.

106-107 There are ten balloons.

108-109 Spot the ticket office

110-111 Spot the toy shop

113

Marvel at the Museum

120–121 There are four actors.

122–123 There are four horses.

126 Three is the odd one out.

Let's Get Building!

130–131 There are five shovels.

134–135 Spot the heavy roller

136–137 Spot who dropped a sandwich

140–141 Spot the backhoe loader

142 Three is the odd one out.

Who's at the Zoo?

150–151 Spot the peacock

157

A Garden to Explore

162–163 Spot the tallest sunflower

165 There are eight holes in the leaf.

166–167 There are four squirrels.

172 Five is the odd one out.

173

3, 2, 1, Blast Off to Space!

176–177 Eight astronauts are wearing helmets.

178–179 Spot the slipper

188 Three is the odd one out.

189